Douglas Weiss, Ph.D.

Recovery
For Everyone

Steps

Recovery for Everyone: Steps
© 2014 by Douglas Weiss
Published by Discovery Press
P.O. Box 51055
Colorado Springs, CO 80949
719-278-3708

Interior and Cover Design By: Janelle Evangelides

Contents

Introduction

The Twelve Steps have helped millions of people recover from such addictions as alcohol, drugs, food, sex, and many others. This workbook takes us thoughtfully through our own personal recovery from addiction. These steps allow us to work at our own pace or with others from your Christian Recovery group. Our prayer is that you will experience hope and strength as you take your personal journey to recover so you can once again experience the joy that Christ has promised you.

Other materials that are available through Heart to Heart Counseling Center which may also be helpful in your recovery are listed in the Appendix of this book. Telephone counseling at Heart to Heart Counseling Center is also available nationwide.

For further information please contact us at the following address or call us at 719-278-3708. You can also visit us on our website at drdougweiss.com or e-mail us at heart2heart@xc.org.

Heart to Heart Counseling Center
P.O. Box 51055
Colorado Springs, CO 80949

Step #1

"We admitted we were powerless over our addiction--
that our lives had become unmanageable."

We

When asked how to pray, Jesus said "Our Father." Jesus understood the need for us to have a corporate vision rather than an individual perspective of God. When the apostle Paul wrote the "one another" (Gal. 5:13, Col. 3:12-13), he understood the need that believers have for each another. Jesus's brother James also understood this when he penned James 5:16, "Confess your faults <u>one to another</u>, and pray <u>one for another</u>, that ye may be healed."

There is healing and spiritual power available as you follow the "we" principle in your life. This is especially true as you take the journey through your recovery from addiction. Addicts generally enjoy doing things by themselves. In recovery, "we" is a new concept for the addict. As a group, "we" can do a lot more than that which can be done alone. Together "we" can heal. When we are left alone it seems we often stay locked into our addiction? We have tried recovery by ourselves with little success, but we can heal together.

We is one of the most important words that this 12 step recovery program has to offer. It is in admitting to ourselves that we are powerless over our addictions and need this new "*we group*" that we can stay sober or clean. The addict has often had other "we groups" before recovery. This is our first topic of discussion.

What are some of the first words that come to your mind when you hear the word *we*?

1. _____ 2. _____ 3. _____

What would you hope to gain from a clean and recovering we group?

1. _____   3. _____

2. _____   4. _____

What kind of peer we groups do you have in your life presently?

1. _____   3. _____

2. _____   4. _____

In the past, have the *we* groups (your friends) been other addicts? List them and tell why they were in your *we* groups?

Addicts	Why?
1. _____	1. _____
2. _____	2. _____
3. _____	3. _____

The concept of *we* can be especially hard for addicts because many have lived so much of their lives isolating themselves and their behaviors from others. When you come into a recovery group you will experience that "*we*" is really obtainable. There are other people who struggle with the same issues as you.

What are some of the feelings you have realizing that you now are not alone in this recovery program?

I felt _____ when _____

When you realized you were not alone in your recovery, a feeling of being known and still being accepted can energize you to the point where you desire to stay in your recovery group.

What are some of the strengths you can see this "we" group adding to your recovery?

1. _____   3. _____

2. _____   4. _____

What are some of the struggles you anticipate when opening up to a group and being honest about your addictive behavior and letting them support you?

1. _____

2. _____

3. _____

Shame over past behavior or not feeling loved (i.e., "If they really knew me, they wouldn't love me." or "I'm not worth helping. You don't know what I did.") can really slow down recovery. The next exercise will assist you from letting those thoughts take over and undermining the progress in your recovery program.

What are goals you can set up to not let shame keep you from being a part of this important recovery "we" group?

1. _____

2. _____

3. _____

4. _____

What other types of *we* groups do you need in your life to stay clean? (Circle)

Alcoholics Anonymous	Freedom Groups	Gamblers Anonymous
Narcotics Anonymous	CODA	Over-Eaters Anonymous
Other _____	Other _____	Other _____

Admitted

Admitted means to acknowledged what already is a fact. We need to admit before we can become and stay clean. In Step One, what are you trying to admit to yourself that is probably already a known fact to others?

1. _____

2. _____

3. _____

Who else possibly already knows this fact?

1. _____

2. _____

3. _____

4. _____

How do they already know what you are admitting about yourself? (For each person listed, give examples of how they may already know about your addiction.)

1. _____

2. _____

3. _____

4. _____

5. _____

Admitting your addiction is one of the hardest things you will ever do! What are some of the feelings you are having about admitting you are an addict?

I feel _____

I feel _____

I feel _____

Until now, what has kept you from admitting to yourself that you are an addict?

1. _____

2. _____

3. _____

Over what particular behaviors are you admitting that you are currently powerless?

1. _____

2. _____

3. _____

4. _____

5. _____

How long have you been addicted to these behaviors? (Example: Alcohol, 15 years)

1. _____

2. _____

3. _____

4. _____

PowerLess

Powerlessness is a state of being that many people do not really accept or even acknowledge. Sometimes we do not even face our powerlessness in the presence of overwhelming facts.

What are some of the facts that lead you to believe that you are *powerless* over your addiction?

1. _____

2. _____

3. _____

4. _____

What does it mean to you to be *powerless* over addiction? Define *powerless*.

_____

_____

_____

What do you think being *powerless* over your addiction will mean to you in the future?

1. _____

2. _____

3. _____

List other people you know that are *powerless* over addiction in their life?

1. _____   3. _____

2. _____   4. _____

Name people who will try to convince you that you are not an addict.

1. _____   3. _____

2. _____   4. _____

How do you intend to respond to those who will try to convince you that you are not an addict?

1. _____

2. _____

3. _____

4. _____

5. _____

What four behaviors demonstrate that you are presently *powerless* over your addiction?

1. _____   3. _____

2. _____   4. _____

If you are unable to list four behavior patterns that presently reflect your powerlessness, why do you believe you are *powerless* over your addiction?

_____

_____

_____

What benefits do you see in being *powerless* over your addiction?

1. _____

2. _____

3. _____

4. _____

5. _____

How do you feel about being *powerless* over your addiction? Why?

I feel _____ because _____

How is being *powerless* over your addiction going to affect the boundaries you set for yourself?

1. _____

2. _____

3. _____

4. _____

5. _____

How is being *powerless* over your addiction going to affect friendships or other relationships?

1. _____

2. _____

3. _____

4. _____

How is being *powerless* over your addiction going to affect your sexual relationship?

1. _____

2. _____

3. _____

4. _____

What are other words that describe *powerless* to you?

1. _____   3. _____

2. _____   4. _____

Realizing that you are *powerless* over your addiction is a big step toward recovery. In taking this step, you will be forced to consider changes in your life, your activities, and even the boundaries you set. How is being *powerless* over your addiction going to affect your life?

1. _____

2. _____

3. _____

4. _____

5. _____

How is being *powerless* over your addiction going to change the activities in your life?

1. _____

2. _____

3. _____

4. _____

5. _____

How is being *powerless* going to affect your entertainment? (T.V., movies, books, parties, other activities)

1. _____

2. _____

3. _____

4. _____

5. _____

What other things or relationships are you *powerless* over other than your addiction?

1. _____

2. _____

3. _____

Unmanageable

Unmanageable is another word we often do not like to hear in our culture. We pride ourselves in being in control. List ways your addiction made you lose control in the following areas of your life.

Spiritual Life

1. _____

2. _____

3. _____

Family relationships

1. _____

2. _____

3. _____

Financial areas

1. _____

2. _____

3. _____

Friendships

1. _____

2. _____

3. _____

Relationship with yourself

1. _____

2. _____

3. _____

Your future

1. _____

2. _____

3. _____

Vocationally

1. _____

2. _____

3. _____

Your spouse

1. _____

2. _____

3. _____

Give examples of when you were unmanageable in your addiction. (Be as specific as possible.)

1. _____

2. _____

3. _____

4. _____

5. _____

What has your addiction cost you? (Other than money)

1. _____

2. _____

3. _____

4. _____

5. _____

What feelings do you have about this?

1. _____

2. _____

3. _____

Who has your addiction affected?

1. _____

2. _____

3. _____

4. _____

5. _____

6. _____

What has your addiction cost the people you listed above?

1. _____

2. _____

3. _____

4. _____

How do you feel about your addiction costing others pain?

I feel _____

I feel _____

I feel _____

Why do you want to recover from your addiction?

1. _____

2. _____

3. _____

4. _____

What do you hope to gain by completing Step One?

1. _____

2. _____

3. _____

Do you feel you were truthful while completing this step? Why or why not?

_____

_____

Could you build a new future from the work you have done during Step One? Why?

_____

_____

_____

When and where do you feel you fully experienced Step One? (Give a specific place and time.) If you are unable to identify a particular place and time when you experienced your Step One, what makes you believe you completed it?

_____

_____

What is the most significant thing you have learned about yourself during this step?

_____

_____

On a scale from 1-10, rate yourself on the work you did in Step One.

1   2   3   4   5   6   7   8   9   10

Why? _____

_____

Feedback Form

The following space is provided for feedback from your group on your Step One work. Use this feedback page for reflection or for continued work on your Step One. May your future journey of recovery begin with this first step.

Name of Group Member _____ Rating 1   2   3   4   5   6   7   8   9   10

Feedback_____

Name of Group Member _____ Rating 1   2   3   4   5   6   7   8   9   10

Feedback_____

Name of Group Member _____ Rating 1   2   3   4   5   6   7   8   9   10

Feedback_____

Name of Group Member _____ Rating 1   2   3   4   5   6   7   8   9   10

Feedback_____

Name of Group Member _____ Rating 1   2   3   4   5   6   7   8   9   10

Feedback_____

Name of Group Member _____ Rating 1   2   3   4   5   6   7   8   9   10

Feedback_____

Name of Group Member _____ Rating 1   2   3   4   5   6   7   8   9   10

Feedback_____

Name of Group Member _____ Rating 1   2   3   4   5   6   7   8   9   10

Feedback_____

Step #2

"Came to believe that a Power greater than ourselves
could restore us to sanity."

Came

The verb *came* in Step Two is in the past tense. This word implies the action has already happened. This means that in this step we are receiving a report of a past event. Highlight in the below spaces examples of God's grace and how he revealed Himself to you when you became a believer in Jesus Christ as your Lord and Savior. (i.e., Being witnessed to, exposed to Christian events, etc.)

1. _____

2. _____

3. _____

4. _____

5. _____

6. _____

7. _____

8. _____

9. _____

10._____

Believe

To believe is to grow or change. Since you came to believe in Jesus Christ as your Lord and Savior, what areas of personal growth have occurred since you came to believe? List them on the following page.

1. _____

2. _____

3. _____

4. _____

A Power Greater

The phrase *A Power Greater* was the only change of wording in the Twelve Steps from it's original writing. The first writing of the Twelve Steps, which began in an Oxford Bible Study and which birthed AA, read "God" instead of "A Power Greater." The change was made because of the stigma that alcoholics had in the 1930's. To be an alcoholic was very shaming at that time in history. For the alcoholic to go to "God" with his shame was very difficult so the writers of the Twelve Steps made the phrase *A Power Greater* instead to give the alcoholic a little time to develop a *God* concept. The support groups allow God to patiently reveal Himself to them. Christians can begin to use Christ in their recovery. Bringing Christ into your recovery is also a process.

Give specific examples of coming to a point of belief in Jesus in different areas of your life.

1. _____

2. _____

3. _____

What were the results of your faith in these areas of your life?

1. _____

2. _____

3. _____

How has your coming to Christ affected your attitudes?

_____

_____

How has your coming to believe in Jesus Christ affected your behavior in the past and present?

1. _____

2. _____

3. _____

How has your coming to believe in Jesus Christ affected your relationships in the past or present with those listed below?

Yourself

1. _____

2. _____

3. _____

Spouse

1. _____

2. _____

3. _____

Children

1. _____

2. _____

3. _____

Parents

1. _____

2. _____

3. _____

Work Relationships

1. _____

2. _____

3. _____

When did you come to believe in Jesus Christ? (Approximate date)

_____

What happened exactly?

_____

_____

_____

How would you define "greater"?

_____

_____

How do you understand the word or concept of power?

_____

_____

_____

What are the powers that are greater than yourself? Why?

1. _____

2. _____

3. _____

What characteristics of Jesus Christ do you believe in?

1. _____

2. _____

3. _____

4. _____

5. _____

How do you know you can believe in Jesus Christ? Be specific as to how He has revealed His power to you.

1. _____

2. _____

3. _____

4. _____

5. _____

6. _____

How do you intend to utilize this relationship with Jesus Christ in your recovery from addiction?

_____

_____

If you had this relationship in the past, what led you away from it?

_____

_____

How long have you been away from your relationship with Jesus Christ?

_____

_____

_____

How did you feel about being away from Him?

1. I felt _____

Explain how you have experienced Jesus Christ to be greater than all of yourself since you have chosen recovery?

1. _____

2. _____

3. _____

Explain your current relationship with Jesus Christ. _____

_____

_____

_____

What activities or behaviors are involved in your relationship with Him?

1. _____

2. _____

3. _____

4. _____

5. _____

6. _____

How much time in a day or a week do you invest in with Jesus Christ?

In a Day _____   In a Week _____

Could

What does it mean to you to believe that Jesus Christ *could* do something to influence your recovery?

_____

_____

In what ways do you see Jesus Christ becoming involved in your addiction recovery?

1. _____

2. _____

3. _____

4. _____

Restore

What does the word *restore* mean to you? _____

_____

In what ways would Jesus have to *restore* you in the following areas of your life?

Spiritually _____

_____

_____

Fun _____

_____

_____

Parenting _____

_____

_____

Financially _____

_____

_____

Sexually _____

_____

_____

Friendships _____

_____

_____

Relationship with Yourself _____

_____

_____

Your Future _____

_____

Marriage _____

_____

_____

What do you hope to gain by completing Step Two?

1. _____

2. _____

3. _____

Do you feel you were truthful while completing this step? Why or why not?

_____

_____

Could you build a new future from the work you have done? Why?

_____

_____

_____

What is the most significant thing you have learned about yourself during this step?

_____

_____

On a scale from 1-10, rate yourself on the work you did in Step Two.

1 2 3 4 5 6 7 8 9 10

Why? _____

_____

Feedback Form

The following space is provided for feedback from your group on your Step One work. Use this feedback page for reflection or for continued work on your Step One. May your future journey of recovery begin with this first step.

Name of Group Member _____ Rating 1 2 3 4 5 6 7 8 9 10

Feedback _____

Name of Group Member _____ Rating 1 2 3 4 5 6 7 8 9 10

Feedback _____

Name of Group Member _____ Rating 1 2 3 4 5 6 7 8 9 10

Feedback _____

Name of Group Member _____ Rating 1 2 3 4 5 6 7 8 9 10

Feedback _____

Name of Group Member _____ Rating 1 2 3 4 5 6 7 8 9 10

Feedback _____

Name of Group Member _____ Rating 1 2 3 4 5 6 7 8 9 10

Feedback _____

Name of Group Member _____ Rating 1 2 3 4 5 6 7 8 9 10

Feedback _____

Name of Group Member _____ Rating 1 2 3 4 5 6 7 8 9 10

Feedback _____

Step #3

"Made a decision to turn our will and lives over to the care
of God as we understood Him."

Made

Made is the past tense of the verb "to make." Make can be defined as a process involving effort to build or construct something. There are processes which are involved in making a decision. What are some of the events that have brought you to the point of deciding to turn your life and will over to God?

1. _____

2. _____

3. _____

As an addict, you have turned your will and life over to various things, persons or beliefs. List the things, persons or beliefs to which you had turned your will and life over to in the past. Be specific.

1. _____

2. _____

3. _____

4. _____

Have you made decisions in the past to turn your life over to God? (i.e., "If you get me out of this one...") List them.

1. _____

2. _____

3. _____

Have you had moments of desperation, whether while acting-out or in recovery, when you cried out to God to take control over your life? (i.e., Praying after relapsing) List them.

1. _____

2. _____

3. _____

4. _____

How is this decision different today from those in the past? _____

_____

_____

Since the word *made* is in the past tense, explain how you have been affected since turning your will and life over to the care of God, especially in your addiction. What has changed? What are you doing differently?

1. _____

2. _____

3. _____

4. _____

Making a major decision in your life often requires time and a lot of thought. What were other major decisions you made in the past? How long did it take to make them? (Marriage/divorce/business choices)

1. _____

2. _____

3. _____

4. _____

In the previous cases, where were you when you *made* that final decision?

1. _____

2. _____

3. _____

If Step Three is thought through carefully, it is probably a decision much like marriage or choosing a vocation.

How much time have you put into this step up to this point? _____

_____

Can you identify a specific moment or culminating event that marks when you initially did your Step Three? If so, please explain.

_____

_____

_____

_____

If the previous answer is no, explain how you know you have completed your Step Three.

_____

_____

What areas in your life are you most reluctant to have God in charge?

List these areas and explain.	Why?
1. _____	1. _____
2. _____	2. _____
3. _____	3. _____
4. _____	4. _____
5. _____	5. _____

Explain how you will allow God to have His will in these areas.

1. _____

2. _____

3. _____

4. _____

5. _____

Over what specific behaviors in your life do you want God to be in charge?

1. _____   3. _____

2. _____   4. _____

How do you intend to give Him charge over these behaviors?

1. _____

2. _____

3. _____

4. _____

How are you turning your will to act out in these addicted manners over to God?

_____

_____

_____

When did you turn over your will to God, and how have you been behaving differently since?

_____

_____

Care

What other words come to mind when you hear the word care as it pertains to the "care of God?"

1. _____   3. _____

2. _____   4. _____

How has God cared for you since you have given your will and life to Him?

1. _____

2. _____

3. _____

Has God demonstrated His care for you before you made this decision? If so, list three times.

1. _____

2. _____

3. _____

God

God can sometimes be a scary reality to those in recovery from addiction. On this page, explain God as you understand Him.

_____

_____

_____

_____

_____

_____

_____

What are characteristics you like and dislike about God?

Like?	Dislike?
1. _____	1. _____
2. _____	2. _____
3. _____	3. _____
4. _____	4. _____
5. _____	5. _____

Does God have the freedom to be the final authority in the areas listed below?

Socially	Yes	No		Job	Yes	No
Financially	Yes	No		Parenting	Yes	No
Marriage	Yes	No		Recovery	Yes	No
Dating	Yes	No		Spiritually	Yes	No
Sexually	Yes	No		Other Addictions	Yes	No

Why do you trust God with your will and life? _____

_____

_____

What do you consider to be your will? _____

_____

_____

What do you consider to be your life? _____

_____

What percentage are you turning over and why? _____

Will _____%   Life _____%

As We Understand Him

We can all learn more about God through prayer, reading the Bible, regular church involvement and support groups. Ask four people who have been in recovery for longer than you to describe "God as they understand Him," as He is active in their lives now. Record their responses.

1. _____

2. _____

3. _____

4. _____

How do you presently practice learning more about God?

1. _____

2. _____

3. _____

4. _____

List behaviors or events that demonstrate you have turned your will over to God instead of allowing self-will to do as it pleases.

1. _____

2. _____

3. _____

4. _____

In what way have you turned your life over to God in these areas?

Family _____

_____

Spouse or Dating _____

_____

Sexually _____

_____

Job _____

_____

Future _____

_____

Financially _____

_____

Recovery_____

_____

Socially_____

_____

What is the most significant thing you have learned about yourself in doing your Step Three?

_____

_____

On a scale from 1-10, rate yourself on the work you did in Step Three.

1 2 3 4 5 6 7 8 9 10

Why? _____

_____

On this page, write a letter to God turning your life and will over to Him.

Dear God,

_____

_____

_____

_____

_____

_____

_____

_____

_____

_____

_____

_____

_____

_____

_____

_____

_____

_____

_____

_____

Feedback Form

The following space is provided for feedback from your group on your Step One work. Use this feedback page for reflection or for continued work on your Step One. May your future journey of recovery begin with this first step.

Name of Group Member _____ Rating 1   2   3   4   5   6   7   8   9   10

Feedback_____

Name of Group Member _____ Rating 1   2   3   4   5   6   7   8   9   10

Feedback_____

Name of Group Member _____ Rating 1   2   3   4   5   6   7   8   9   10

Feedback_____

Name of Group Member _____ Rating 1   2   3   4   5   6   7   8   9   10

Feedback_____

Name of Group Member _____ Rating 1   2   3   4   5   6   7   8   9   10

Feedback_____

Name of Group Member _____ Rating 1   2   3   4   5   6   7   8   9   10

Feedback_____

Name of Group Member _____ Rating 1   2   3   4   5   6   7   8   9   10

Feedback_____

Name of Group Member _____ Rating 1   2   3   4   5   6   7   8   9   10

Feedback_____

Step #4

"Made a searching and fearless moral inventory of ourselves"

Made

By the end of Step Four we will have *made* (past tense) a moral inventory of ourselves. Many addicts in the midst of their addiction did not have the clarity of mind to distinguish between moral or immoral behavior. It is now necessary to do so, lest the guilt or grandiosity pulls you back into your addiction. List strengths and weaknesses you may have in the following areas of your life.

List strengths and weaknesses you have in the spiritual areas of your life.

Strengths

1. _____
2. _____
3. _____
4. _____

Weaknesses

1. _____
2. _____
3. _____
4. _____

List strengths and weaknesses you have in the financial areas of your life.

Strengths

1. _____
2. _____
3. _____
4. _____

Weaknesses

1. _____
2. _____
3. _____
4. _____

List strengths and weaknesses you have in your relationships.

Strengths

1. _____

Weaknesses

1. _____

2. _____   2. _____

3. _____   3. _____

4. _____   4. _____

List strengths and weaknesses you have in your marital relationship.

Strengths   Weaknesses

1. _____   1. _____

2. _____   2. _____

3. _____   3. _____

4. _____   4. _____

List strengths and weaknesses you have in your vocation.

Strengths   Weaknesses

1. _____   1. _____

2. _____   2. _____

3. _____   3. _____

4. _____   4. _____

List strengths and weaknesses you have had in relating to your Mother.

Strengths   Weaknesses

1. _____   1. _____

2. _____   2. _____

3. _____   3. _____

4. _____   4. _____

List strengths and weaknesses you have had in relating to your Father.

Strengths   Weaknesses

1. _____   1. _____

2. _____   2. _____

3. _____   3. _____

4. _____   4. _____

List strengths and weaknesses you have had in relating to your Siblings.

Strengths   Weaknesses

1. _____   1. _____

2. _____   2. _____

3. _____   3. _____

4. _____   4. _____

List strengths and weaknesses you have had in relating to Yourself.

Strengths   Weaknesses

1. _____   1. _____

2. _____   2. _____

3. _____   3. _____

4. _____   4. _____

List strengths and weaknesses you have had in relating sexually with your spouse.

Strengths   Weaknesses

1. _____   1. _____

2. _____   2. _____

3. _____   3. _____

4. _____   4. _____

List strengths and weaknesses you have had in relating to Authorities.

Strengths   Weaknesses

1. _____   1. _____

2. _____   2. _____

3. _____   3._____

4. _____   4._____

The above assessment gives an idea of how positive or negative your behaviors have been toward yourself and others. There is yet another inventory to fearlessly take in this step. This inventory is a deliberate search for additional moral information about yourself.

You will need to be alert as you look at strengths, shortcomings or losses you have had up to this point in your life. These losses may not have been intentional but have nevertheless caused losses toward others. You may have suffered a loss of innocence by being sexually abused or sexually abusing others.

Losses

Inventory your losses in one column including harm that was done to you or harm that you may have caused toward others. This could include abuse (physical, sexual, emotional), divorce, affairs, death of a loved one, losses, being adopted or abandoned by a parent, school or legal issues, sexual activity, and other significant events.

In another column list positive events such as school events, career advancements, marriage, and the birth of children. Be specific. Include what happened, with whom, and feelings then and now about the event.

Ages 1-6

Losses   Strengths

_____   _____

_____   _____

_____   _____

_____   _____

Ages 7-12

Losses   Strengths

_____   _____

_____   _____

_____   _____

_____   _____

_____   _____

Ages 13-15

Losses

_____

_____

_____

_____

_____

_____

Strengths

_____

_____

_____

_____

_____

_____

Ages 16-25

Losses

_____

_____

_____

_____

_____

_____

_____

Strengths

_____

_____

_____

_____

_____

_____

_____

Age 26-35

Losses

_____

_____

Strengths

_____

_____

_____

_____

_____

_____

_____

_____

_____

_____

_____

_____

Ages 36-45

Losses

Strengths

_____

_____

_____

_____

_____

_____

_____

_____

_____

_____

_____

_____

_____

_____

Ages 46-55

Losses

Strengths

_____

_____

_____

_____

_____

_____

_____

_____

_____

_____

_____

_____

_____

Ages 56 to 65

Losses

_____

_____

_____

_____

_____

_____

_____

Strengths

_____

_____

_____

_____

_____

_____

_____

Ages 66 or better

Losses

_____

_____

_____

_____

_____

_____

_____

Strengths

_____

_____

_____

_____

_____

_____

_____

Have you been 100% honest in writing down the losses that you are aware of?

Yes _____   No _____

Are there specific things you were too ashamed to write down at this point in your recovery?

Yes _____   No _____

Have you been sexually abused by a male?

Yes _____   No _____

Did you include this in your inventory?

Yes _____   No _____

Were you sexually abused by a female older than yourself when you were a child?

Yes _____   No _____

Describe your first sexual encounter. _____

_____

_____

Ourselves

The recovering community can help us learn much about *ourselves*. Contact four recovering people who have completed Step Four and ask the what they learned about themselves during this step. Record their first name and answers in the space provided below.

1. _____

2. _____

3. _____

4. _____
What have you learned in this step about the word ourselves?

1. _____

2. _____

3. _____

4. _____

What specifically have you learned about yourself?

1. _____

2. _____

What is the most significant thing you have learned about yourself in completing your Step Four?

_____

_____

On a scale from 1-10, rate yourself on the work you did in Step Four.

1 2 3 4 5 6 7 8 9 10

Why? _____

_____

Feedback Form

The following space is provided for feedback from your group on your Step One work. Use this feedback page for reflection or for continued work on your Step One. May your future journey of recovery begin with this first step.

Name of Group Member _____ Rating 1 2 3 4 5 6 7 8 9 10

Feedback_____

Name of Group Member _____ Rating 1 2 3 4 5 6 7 8 9 10

Feedback_____

Name of Group Member _____ Rating 1 2 3 4 5 6 7 8 9 10

Feedback_____

Name of Group Member _____ Rating 1 2 3 4 5 6 7 8 9 10

Feedback_____

Name of Group Member _____ Rating 1 2 3 4 5 6 7 8 9 10

Feedback_____

Name of Group Member _____ Rating 1 2 3 4 5 6 7 8 9 10

Feedback_____

Name of Group Member _____ Rating 1 2 3 4 5 6 7 8 9 10

Feedback_____

Name of Group Member _____ Rating 1 2 3 4 5 6 7 8 9 10

Feedback_____

Step #5

"Admitted to God, to ourselves, and to another human being the exact nature of our wrongs."

So far in your journey you have been either reunited or for the first time introduced to Jesus. This will help you to admit to Him the exact nature of your wrongs. The journey through Step Four gave you some awareness of yourself. Step Five will further aid you in this understanding.

Admitting

Admitting can often be the hardest thing to do. Are there reasons you would like not to entirely admit the exact nature of your wrongs? (i.e., fear of being rejected if others knew, or if the behavior was against the law?) List these.

1. _____

2. _____

3. _____

If you have written anything in the last question, get feedback from recovering people who have already gone through Step Five. How did they deal with these issues?

1. _____

2. _____

3. _____

If you did not write anything for the above question, ask four recovering people who have done their Step Five what some of their experiences were in doing this step.

1. _____

2. _____

3. _____

Ask these same people what feelings they had <u>after</u> doing their Step Five.

1. _____

2. _____

3. _____

Now we come to an hour of reckoning. Often, to our own harm as addicts, we continuously carry a list of things we have done wrong. It is now time to write this list on paper. Make a list of people you are aware of that you have wronged and their relationship to you.

Name	Relationship
_____	_____
_____	_____
_____	_____
_____	_____
_____	_____

Write exactly what you did wrong to each of them. Remember to list exactly each wrong done. Use additional paper if necessary.

Name	Relation	Wrong Done
_____	_____	_____
_____	_____	_____
_____	_____	_____
_____	_____	_____

Now that you have looked at your wrongs from a relational point of view, it is time to look at them chronologically. On the following pages, in chronological order, write the names of those you have wronged physically, sexually, emotionally, etc. Use your Step Four to help you in this process.

In the space provided, list names of people wronged and a brief explanation of the exact wrong. Include those on previous pages.

Age 1-6

_____

_____

_____

_____

_____

_____

_____

_____

Ages 7-12

_____

_____

_____

_____

_____

_____

_____

_____

_____

_____

_____

_____

_____

_____

_____

_____

_____

_____

_____

_____

_____

_____

_____

_____

_____

_____

_____

Ages 16-25

_____

_____

_____

_____

_____

_____

_____

_____

_____

_____

_____

_____

_____

_____

_____

_____

_____

_____

Ages 36-45

_____

_____

_____

_____

_____

_____

_____

_____

_____

_____

_____

_____

_____

_____

_____

_____

_____

_____

_____

_____

Ages 46-55

Ages 56-65

Ages 66 or better

_____

_____

_____

_____

_____

_____

_____

_____

_____

_____

_____

_____

_____

_____

_____

_____

_____

I feel _____

I feel _____

How do you feel about yourself?

I feel _____

I feel _____

On a scale from 1-10, rate yourself on the work you did in Step Five.

1 2 3 4 5 6 7 8 9 10

Why? _____

_____

Feedback Form

The following space is provided for feedback from your group on your Step One work. Use this feedback page for reflection or for continued work on your Step One. May your future journey of recovery begin with this first step.

Name of Group Member _____ Rating 1   2   3   4   5   6   7   8   9   10

Feedback_____

Name of Group Member _____ Rating 1   2   3   4   5   6   7   8   9   10

Feedback_____

Name of Group Member _____ Rating 1   2   3   4   5   6   7   8   9   10

Feedback_____

Name of Group Member _____ Rating 1   2   3   4   5   6   7   8   9   10

Feedback_____

Name of Group Member _____ Rating 1   2   3   4   5   6   7   8   9   10

Feedback_____

Name of Group Member _____ Rating 1   2   3   4   5   6   7   8   9   10

Feedback_____

Name of Group Member _____ Rating 1   2   3   4   5   6   7   8   9   10

Feedback_____

Name of Group Member _____ Rating 1   2   3   4   5   6   7   8   9   10

Feedback_____

Step #6

"Were entirely ready to have God remove all these defects of character."

Entirely

When we think of the word *entirely*, many pictures come to mind. One of the most vivid pictures is that of a sprint runner who has his foot on the block and hands in the dirt in front of the white line while listening for the gun which is ready to go off. This is an appropriate picture for *entirely*. *Entirely* is 100% ready to do something. Many addicts in the midst of their addiction have been *entirely ready* to destroy themselves for the high, the fix, the relationship or the avoidance of pain from the past.

Now you have come to another point in your life where you need to be *entirely ready* after completing Steps One through Five to do something to better yourself.

What are some of the words you think of when you think of the word *entirely*?

1. _____

2. _____

3. _____

What are some of the feelings you have when you think of the word *entirely*?

I feel _____

I feel _____

What are a couple of examples in your life when you were *entirely ready* to do something? (Be specific.)

_____

_____

_____

To Have God (Jesus)

Who has Jesus become to you during your journey through Steps One through Five?

_____

_____

_____

What roles is He filling in your life?

_____

_____

What feelings do you have towards Jesus at this point?

_____

_____

Why do you think that you need *to have God* involved in this part of the recovery process?

_____

_____

How have you relied upon Jesus in the past?

_____

_____

What aspects or characteristics of God are you relying upon to help in the process of removing your defects of character?

_____

_____

Remove

Remove is another word in recovery that can mean something very painful for an addict. An analogy of *Remove* could be to remove weeds from your grass by pulling them up. Another picture could be to remove a tumor that in the future could have killed you.

What are some of the words you think of when you think of the word *remove*?

1. _____

2. _____

3. _____

4. _____

What are some of the feelings you have when you think of something being removed from you?

I feel _____

I feel _____

What are some of the things that have been removed from you up to this point in your addiction recovery?

1. _____

2. _____

3. _____

How do you feel about these things being removed?

_____

_____

How has God been involved in the removal process?

_____

_____

ALL

All means quite a bit to anyone in recovery. It is going to mean a lot also in Step Six. What are some words that come to your mind when you think of the word *all*?

1. _____

2. _____

3. _____

What percentage is *all*? _____%

What percentage do you want *all* to mean when you talk about removing your defects of character? _____%

Defects

Defects basically are shortcomings or flaws. It doesn't mean we are any less lovable or less human. Actually, like the diamond, no matter how valuable or big the diamond is, it has carbon spots in it somewhere. All of us are going to have carbon spots in our life. This is part of being human. This is not something to be ashamed about nor is it something to be proud about. However, it is something we can accept and at this point identify for ourselves.

What are some of the defects that you have seen in your past?

Ages 1-20

1. _____

2. _____

3. _____

4. _____

5. _____

Ages 21-30

1. _____

2. _____

3. _____

4. _____

5. _____

Ages 31-40

1. _____

2. _____

3. _____

4. _____

5. _____

Ages 41-50

1. _____

2. _____

3. _____

4. _____

5. _____

Ages 51 or better

1. _____

2. _____

3. _____

4. _____

5. _____

What are some of the *defects* you have in relating to the following people or areas of your life?

Yourself

1. _____

2. _____

3. _____

Your family of origin (parents)

1. _____

2. _____

3. _____

Your spouse

1. _____

2. _____

3. _____

Your children

1. _____

2. _____

3. _____

Your employer

1. _____

2. _____

3. _____

Your spiritual authorities

1. _____

2. _____

3. _____

Your friends

1. _____

2. _____

3. _____

Your Lord

1. _____

2. _____

3. _____

Below, compile a full list of these defects of character, the length of time you have been aware of their existence, and the percentage at this point that you are willing to have them removed. An example is given below.

Example:	Defects	Length of Time	Percentage
	Self willed	32 years	80-90%

Defects	Length of Time	Percentage
_____	_____	_____
_____	_____	_____
_____	_____	_____
_____	_____	_____
_____	_____	_____
_____	_____	_____
_____	_____	_____
_____	_____	_____
_____	_____	_____
_____	_____	_____
_____	_____	_____
_____	_____	_____
_____	_____	_____
_____	_____	_____
_____	_____	_____

Set some time aside for each one of these character defects and write a paragraph on what life would be like without this defect in your life. Use the below lines to summarize your writings.

_____

_____

_____

_____

_____

_____

_____

_____

_____

Write below the character defects that you are 100% *ready to have God remove*. This list would include the character defects that if God would take them from you, you would let Him have them and not want to take them back.

_____   _____   _____

_____   _____   _____

_____   _____   _____

_____   _____   _____

After a time of prayer and meditation regarding your character defects, write the date below that you became *entirely ready* for Him to remove all the defects.

_____/_____/_____

Place how long each character defect has been in your life. Now looking at these defects of character, what percentage on each one of these defects are you ready to have God remove? Write a percentage by each one.

_____   _____   _____

_____   _____   _____

_____   _____   _____

_____   _____   _____

Character

Character is what we are as a person. As we discussed before, there are carbon spots and these spots are important for us to identify. If we know where the spots are, we can surely ask God to help us with them.

This ends our journey on Step Six. All Step Six requests from us is to become *entirely ready to have God remove all our defects of character*. So far we have listed our defects and thought through what it would be like to have them removed.

What is the most significant thing you have learned about yourself in completing Step Six?

_____

_____

On a scale from 1-10, rate yourself on the work you did in Step Six.

1 2 3 4 5 6 7 8 9 10

Why? _____

_____

Feedback Form

The following space is provided for feedback from your group on your Step One work. Use this feedback page for reflection or for continued work on your Step One. May your future journey of recovery begin with this first step.

Name of Group Member _____ Rating 1 2 3 4 5 6 7 8 9 10

Feedback _____

Name of Group Member _____ Rating 1 2 3 4 5 6 7 8 9 10

Feedback _____

Name of Group Member _____ Rating 1 2 3 4 5 6 7 8 9 10

Feedback _____

Name of Group Member _____ Rating 1 2 3 4 5 6 7 8 9 10

Feedback _____

Name of Group Member _____ Rating 1 2 3 4 5 6 7 8 9 10

Feedback _____

Name of Group Member _____ Rating 1 2 3 4 5 6 7 8 9 10

Feedback _____

Name of Group Member _____ Rating 1 2 3 4 5 6 7 8 9 10

Feedback _____

Name of Group Member _____ Rating 1 2 3 4 5 6 7 8 9 10

Feedback _____

Step #7

"Humbly asked Him to remove our shortcomings."

Humbly

Humbly can mean a disposition, an attitude, a reverence or submissiveness. I can remember a couple of past educational experiences where I was called into the principal's office and there appeared to be a feeling of humbleness while waiting to go into his office. It was the feeling of knowing that this person can impact my life. An authority figure can have an effect on me and have the authority to do something either positively or negatively, and I am at that person's disposal. Many have experienced something similar to this in their lives at some point. The scriptures are very clear about the virtue of humbleness in Col. 3:12, James 4:7-10, and I Pet. 5:5-6.

What are some of the experiences you have had that caused you to feel *humble*?

1. _____

2. _____

3. _____

What are the feelings that accompanied you in those experiences when you were humbled?

I felt _____

I felt _____

When was the last time you were in an experience like that?

_____

Asked

There is an old saying, "You have not because you asked not." This is also true as it relates to our recovery in Step Seven. Many addicts have never honestly looked at their character defects or limitations. On the following pages we will search further in the meaning of *asked*.

What are some of the things that you have asked of God before and you received them?

1. _____

2. _____

3. _____

Many times it takes "faith," "trust," or even "hope" in asking. Some have felt so desperate and full of despair because of some of the shortcomings in their past or current life and feel as if there is no way out. Now we come to a point where we can ask. Asking doesn't always mean it is going to happen the way we want it to nor that we are going to be in control of the procedure. But let's look at the possibility of asking.

What are some of the things in this step that you would like to ask for?

1. _____

2. _____

3. _____

4. _____

5. _____

6. _____

7. _____

8. _____

9. _____

10. _____

Him

What are some of the aspects of God you are clinging to as you ask *Him* to do these things for you?

_____

_____

Have you experienced these characteristics before in your relationship to God? If so, how?

1. _____

2. _____

3. _____

4. _____

5. _____

Remove

We talked about the word *remove* in Step Six. This is when we ask for it to actually happen. We are beyond "entirely ready." An analogy of this removal process would be similar to being on a physician's table asking Him to cut into us and *remove* the cancer which ails us. We are now asking Him to cut deep into our mind and our own will and *remove*. During this surgical procedure, there may be a variety of experiences that you may have.

What are some of the experiences you are anticipating to happen?

1. _____

2. _____

3. _____

Have you had any experience with God removing anything else in your life? Yes _____ No _____

If so, explain what and how He removed it.

_____

_____

Did you believe that He would do the removal the way He did? Yes _____ No _____

It is true that the removal process is somewhat of a mystery. Who would think that to create patience you would experience situations that would cause you to become patient? Who would think that in the process of becoming kind, you would have to actually change or behave in a new way?

Many of the processes which God is going to use in our life are not in our control, nor should they be. The removing is not our doing. It is clear that we are asking someone else to do something much like asking a surgeon to fix something. We don't have the insight nor the education that these surgeons would have nor would many of us want it. We just have to trust that they can do what we are asking them to do.

Have you seen God remove things in other people's lives? Yes _____ No _____

Was he successful in these surgeries? Yes _____ No _____

What are some of the feelings you have about God being in control of removing the things that you have listed as being 100% ready to remove in Step Six?

I feel _____

I feel _____

Our

The word *Our* is one of the great words of the Twelve Steps. It means that there is more than just one person who has gone through this. You are not alone, nor will you ever be.

Who are some of the people you know who have done their Step Seven?

1. _____

2. _____

3. _____

4. _____

What were some of their experiences after going through Step Seven? List These.

1. _____

2. _____

3. _____

4. _____

Shortcomings

Shortcomings are similar to defects. They are the carbon spots or issues identified in Step Six. Review your Step Six and look carefully over the character defects you identified as being 100% ready to have God remove. Write out your prayer to God to remove one character defect at a time. Don't rob yourself and try to clump them all together. Ask Him to take His knowledge and ways to systematically remove them and give Him full permission to rank them in the order He sees most important and viable. It is much like surgery. Sometimes the surgeon has to prioritize what is going on within the system. If someone has been shot, the surgeon has to look past something else to get at what is primary. Allow God to prioritize as he removes these aspects.

Write below in the spaces provided the list of defects that you have already prayed about. In one year, come back to this and see how much work God has done.

Defects	Date Prayed For Removal	My One Year Progress Note
_____	_____	_____
_____	_____	_____
_____	_____	_____
_____	_____	_____
_____	_____	_____
_____	_____	_____
_____	_____	_____
_____	_____	_____
_____	_____	_____
_____	_____	_____
_____	_____	_____
_____	_____	_____
_____	_____	_____
_____	_____	_____
_____	_____	_____
_____	_____	_____
_____	_____	_____
_____	_____	_____

What is the most significant thing you've learned about yourself while completing Step Seven?

_____

_____

On a scale from 1-10, rate yourself on the work you did in Step Seven.

1   2   3   4   5   6   7   8   9   10

Why? _____

_____

Feedback Form

The following space is provided for feedback from your group on your Step One work. Use this feedback page for reflection or for continued work on your Step One. May your future journey of recovery begin with this first step.

Name of Group Member _____ Rating 1 2 3 4 5 6 7 8 9 10

Feedback_____

Name of Group Member _____ Rating 1 2 3 4 5 6 7 8 9 10

Feedback_____

Name of Group Member _____ Rating 1 2 3 4 5 6 7 8 9 10

Feedback_____

Name of Group Member _____ Rating 1 2 3 4 5 6 7 8 9 10

Feedback_____

Name of Group Member _____ Rating 1 2 3 4 5 6 7 8 9 10

Feedback_____

Name of Group Member _____ Rating 1 2 3 4 5 6 7 8 9 10

Feedback_____

Name of Group Member _____ Rating 1 2 3 4 5 6 7 8 9 10

Feedback_____

Name of Group Member _____ Rating 1 2 3 4 5 6 7 8 9 10

Feedback_____

Step #8

"Made a list of all people we had harmed,
and became willing to make amends to them all"

Made a List

Thus far throughout the 12 Steps, we have made a decision to turn our life over to the care of God and made a searching and fearless inventory. Now we come to a time where we are going to *make a list*.

Of All People

Again, we are confronted with the word *all*. *All* means 100% in this case. This includes people in your past and present that you may have victimized or hurt through your own addiction issues.

We

Again it is very comforting to see the word *We* confirming that you are not the only person who may have caused others harm because of your addiction issues. Harm is a difficult word for many addicts and that is why it is here in Step Eight that we will address this. If you would have done this step earlier, you probably would not have been sober enough to realize that your attitudes and behaviors actually inflicted pain whether knowingly or unknowingly. You may have caused many people whom you have known, loved and deeply cared about a tremendous amount of shame or hurt. It is now time to look at the harm that has been done to others while in your addiction.

Lets take a sober moment and consider prayer, asking God to help you to make this list. We will make this list chronological in order. This is similar to your list in Step Four. Now would be a good time to go back to Step Four and review the things you have done and the people you have hurt. Make a list of these people

Ages 1-12

1. _____

2. _____

3. _____

4. _____

Ages 13-20

1. _____
2. _____
3. _____
4. _____
5. _____
6. _____
7. _____
8. _____
9. _____
10. _____

Ages 21-30

1. _____
2. _____
3. _____
4. _____
5. _____
6. _____
7. _____
8. _____
9. _____
10. _____

Ages 31-40

1. _____
2. _____
3. _____
4. _____
5. _____

Ages 41-50

1. _____
2. _____
3. _____
4. _____
5. _____

Ages 51-60

1. _____
2. _____
3. _____
4. _____
5. _____

Ages 61 and better

1. _____
2. _____
3. _____
4. _____
5. _____

Take time to compile a list of people you may have caused pain to more than once.

1. _____

2. _____

3. _____

4. _____

5. _____

6. _____

7. _____

8. _____

9. _____

10. _____

And

And is a great conjunction. I am glad that we didn't stop at just making this list. If we did, it would be possibly too painful to bear.

How do you feel about making your list?

I feel _____

I feel _____

Became

This is a process. It takes time. Give yourself permission to become willing to make amends. This is similar to Step Four and Five where you are reckoning a part of yourself. How did you feel after you completed Step Five?'

I felt _____

I felt _____

Willing

We have talked about the word *willing* indirectly in Step Six when we discussed being "entirely ready." *Willing* means that you are, regardless of emotion, willing to submit or comply to what needs to be done. This doesn't mean that you are going to do it yet, just that you are *willing*. For those who exercise, it is similar to lying in bed and at some point become *willing* to get up and then move into the direction of going to exercise. We don't arrive at the gym immediately but do begin moving in that direction.

What are some experiences you have had in becoming *willing* during your recovery?

1. _____

2. _____

3. _____

What were the results of this willingness?

1. _____

2. _____

3. _____

Make Amends

An amend is making something right again, to restore or try to mend something that has been broken. Many of us will do this as we move from our Step Eight to our Step Nine. Part of Step Eight is that we become willing to make that step and mend what has been broken and acknowledge our responsibility in the breaking of it.

To Them All

What percentage is all? _____%

Make a list of these people again.

1. _____ _____ %   11. _____ _____ %

2. _____ _____ %   12. _____ _____ %

3. _____ _____ %   13. _____ _____ %

4. _____ _____ %   14. _____ _____ %

5. _____ _____ %   15. _____ _____ %

6. _____ _____ %   16. _____ _____ %

7. _____ _____ %   17. _____ _____ %

8. _____ _____ %   18. _____ _____ %

9. _____ _____ %   19. _____ _____ %

10. _____ _____ %   20. _____ _____ %

Use this list regularly until you become 100% willing to make amends to them all. Prayerfully consider this as you become willing.

Some people in recovery stay at Step Eight for some time until they become willing to make amends to them all. There are some experiences that are quite painful. Step Eight is to get us to the point where we are willing. Below write the date when you became 100% willing to make amends to every person on this list.

_____

What is the most significant thing you have learned about yourself in completing your Step Eight?

_____

_____

On a scale from 1-10, rate yourself on the work you did in Step Eight.

1 2 3 4 5 6 7 8 9 10

Why? _____

_____

Feedback Form

The following space is provided for feedback from your group on your Step One work. Use this feedback page for reflection or for continued work on your Step One. May your future journey of recovery begin with this first step.

Name of Group Member _____ Rating 1 2 3 4 5 6 7 8 9 10

Feedback _____

Name of Group Member _____ Rating 1 2 3 4 5 6 7 8 9 10

Feedback _____

Name of Group Member _____ Rating 1 2 3 4 5 6 7 8 9 10

Feedback _____

Name of Group Member _____ Rating 1 2 3 4 5 6 7 8 9 10

Feedback _____

Name of Group Member _____ Rating 1 2 3 4 5 6 7 8 9 10

Feedback _____

Name of Group Member _____ Rating 1 2 3 4 5 6 7 8 9 10

Feedback _____

Name of Group Member _____ Rating 1 2 3 4 5 6 7 8 9 10

Feedback _____

Name of Group Member _____ Rating 1 2 3 4 5 6 7 8 9 10

Feedback _____

Step #9

"Made direct amends to such people where ever possible,
except when to do so would injure them or others."

Made

This is the last time the word *made* is used in our Twelve Step journey and it may also be the most painful. Now we will turn our energies, creativity and time into making direct amends to those we have harmed.

Direct

What are some words you think of when you hear the word *direct*?

1. _____

2. _____

3. _____

What are some words that come to mind that are opposite of *direct*?

1. _____

2. _____

3. _____

How do you feel about the opposite words of direct especially when someone is that way toward you?

I feel _____

I feel _____

How do you feel about someone who is being *direct* toward you?

I feel _____

I feel _____

Direct is definitely the straightest line between any two points. In the past most addicts have been vague, shamed and blamed and have avoided and rationalized many behaviors. Some defense mechanisms may have been to blame others for their behaviors. Some rationalized why they behaved that way and why they weren't responsible. Some minimized their behaviors and were not able to see the damage done in other people's lives. These defense mechanisms helped quite a bit to stay in addiction but holds no hope in recovery. Lets discuss what *direct* means.

The most *direct* formula in recovery as it relates to these amends is as follows.

1. Face to face contact: Talk to the person, face to face, and have a discussion regarding what you had done that caused them harm. This is the most direct amend that can be made in a relationship. This is by far the best method of being direct with your amends.

2. Phone calls: If the person is too far to travel to make a direct amend, then a phone call can suffice as a second most direct amend.

3. Letter: For the person who does not have a phone, or can not be reached in any other manner, a letter is your least direct amend.

4. Symbolic: Symbolically put the person you are making an amend to in an empty chair facing you and make your amend to them. This would only be for people you don't know or can't contact. Do not use a symbolic amend for non-sexual offenses unless you consult your sponsor or therapist.

Amends

Making *Amends* is a process of fusing two pieces that are broken or at least bringing them into contact. You are not required to restore the relationship. An amend is only you cleaning your side of the street. It does not minimize, rationalize, or blame anyone for the behavior that caused pain. It is you looking fully at the pain that you caused another human being and acknowledging that pain to them. It is asking them to forgive you and advance in the relationship as they wish to. You are not responsible for their forgiveness. You are only 100% responsible for what you did to them.

A word of caution - You may need the help of the group or a therapist to help you decide who you should or should not see. Going to see ex-lovers is not a good idea.

Such People

Make a list of the people from Step Eight and in the columns provided, check off those you can do face-to-face, call, send a letter or do a symbolic amend to.

Name	Face To Face	Call	Letter	Symbolic
1. _____	_____	_____	_____	_____
2. _____	_____	_____	_____	_____
3. _____	_____	_____	_____	_____
4. _____	_____	_____	_____	_____
5. _____	_____	_____	_____	_____
6. _____	_____	_____	_____	_____
7. _____	_____	_____	_____	_____
8. _____	_____	_____	_____	_____
9. _____	_____	_____	_____	_____
10. _____	_____	_____	_____	_____
11. _____	_____	_____	_____	_____
12. _____	_____	_____	_____	_____
13. _____	_____	_____	_____	_____
14. _____	_____	_____	_____	_____
15. _____	_____	_____	_____	_____
16. _____	_____	_____	_____	_____
17. _____	_____	_____	_____	_____
18. _____	_____	_____	_____	_____
17. _____	_____	_____	_____	_____
18. _____	_____	_____	_____	_____
19. _____	_____	_____	_____	_____
20. _____	_____	_____	_____	_____

Wherever Possible

In the 1930's when the steps were written, *wherever possible* was much more limited than today. Today, *wherever possible* is almost everywhere due to planes and technology that enables us to reach anyone in the world. *Wherever possible* is also acknowledging the fact that not everyone who you owe an amend to will be able to be reached, found or located. For this you are not responsible. If you can't locate someone you are no longer responsible to make that amend. If you feel you need to make a symbolic amend, you can write them a letter and read it to them as if they were in a chair in front of you. This may be helpful for you to resolve the issue.

List those people who, after trying, you were not able to locate.

1. _____

2. _____

3. _____

4. _____

5. _____

Except

Except appears to be one of the bigger words to some addicts during this step. Many addicts say "Oh good, a loophole." However, this is not what the word *except* means. This word *except* is used very sparingly. It means that there are some on the list that need to be exceptions. List those that you currently believe would be exceptions because to do so would cause them injury or harm to be aware of these issues now.

1. _____

2. _____

3. _____

4. _____

5. _____

List five people you respect in recovery who have already done their Step Nine.

1. _____

2. _____

3. _____

4. _____

5. _____

After talking to each of the persons you listed above, what are their perceptions of whether your list of exceptions are appropriate? After considering their feedback, list those left that continue to be exempt.

1. _____

2. _____

3. _____

4. _____

5. _____

What is the injury or harm that would be caused if you made an amend to those on your above list?

1. _____

2. _____

3. _____

4. _____

5. _____

After prayer and meditation, do you have peace about those not receiving a direct amend?

Yes _____   No _____

Make a list again of the people you owe amends to. In the column next to their name, list the date you made your amend. Caution: Do not wait but actively pursue this!

Name   Date

1. _____   _____

2. _____   _____

3. _____   _____

4. _____   _____

5. _____   _____

6. _____   _____

7. _____   _____

8. _____   _____

9. _____   _____

10. _____   _____

11. _____   _____

12. _____   _____

13. _____   _____

14. _____   _____

15. _____   _____

16. _____   _____

17. _____   _____

18. _____   _____

19. _____   _____

20. _____   _____

Complete your Step Nine by filling in the dates of all the people on this list. Your Step Nine is not completed until the last date is listed.

How many direct amends can you make in the next week? Month? 3 Months?

1 Week _____   1 Month _____   3 Months _____

What were some of the experiences you had in doing your Step Nine?

_____

_____

_____

What were some of your favorite conversations? _____

_____

_____

_____

_____

_____

_____

_____

_____

What were some of the feelings you had before, during, and after making your amends?

Before, I felt _____

During, I felt _____

After, I felt _____

How do you feel about these relationships after you made your amends?

I feel _____

I feel _____

I feel _____

How do you feel about yourself now in the context of these relationships?

I feel _____

What is the most significant thing you learned about yourself while completing your Step Nine?

_____

_____

On a scale from 1-10, rate yourself on the work you did in Step Nine.

1 2 3 4 5 6 7 8 9 10

Why? _____

_____

Feedback Form

The following space is provided for feedback from your group on your Step One work. Use this feedback page for reflection or for continued work on your Step One. May your future journey of recovery begin with this first step.

Name of Group Member _____ Rating 1 2 3 4 5 6 7 8 9 10

Feedback_____

Name of Group Member _____ Rating 1 2 3 4 5 6 7 8 9 10

Feedback_____

Name of Group Member _____ Rating 1 2 3 4 5 6 7 8 9 10

Feedback_____

Name of Group Member _____ Rating 1 2 3 4 5 6 7 8 9 10

Feedback_____

Name of Group Member _____ Rating 1 2 3 4 5 6 7 8 9 10

Feedback_____

Name of Group Member _____ Rating 1 2 3 4 5 6 7 8 9 10

Feedback_____

Name of Group Member _____ Rating 1 2 3 4 5 6 7 8 9 10

Feedback_____

Name of Group Member _____ Rating 1 2 3 4 5 6 7 8 9 10

Feedback_____

Step #10

"Continued to take personal inventory and when
we were wrong, promptly admitted it"

Continued

Continue is a process that will last a lifetime. Being human means making mistakes. Step Ten allows us to be human without accumulating guilt or shame from behavior or attitudes. Step Ten is a life-style. What is the date you are starting this life-style choice?

Date:_____

Personal Inventory

A personal inventory is a recording of a person's behavior and attitudes. Behavior and attitudes can hurt us as well as others. The other side of our inventory is strengths we may have practiced today. Recovery will enable strengths to grow. In Step Ten, we don't have to proclaim our strengths to others. This is for us to know and to thank God for. In Step Ten we are honest about our mistakes and then admit them to those we made the mistake toward.

Below is a form to use over the next month so that you can get into a healthy habit and make sure that this principle is being applied regularly in your life. You are going to need to continue this behavior throughout your life. Now that we are shameless, we can relate to God more openly than ever before in our recovery.

Day	Amends Asked For	Strength Acknowledged
1		
2		
3		
4		
5		
6		
7		
8		
9		
10		
11		
12		
13		
14		
15		
16		
17		
18		
19		
20		
21		
22		
23		
24		
25		
26		
27		
28		
29		
30		
31		

Your personal inventory is not up at the end of the month. This form is only available to get you into the habit of looking honestly at yourself without shame and help you to say "that was a mistake" and admit it promptly.

Promptly Admitted It

Promptly means in a timely manner. It does not mean weeks or months later. It should not be much longer than the day you made the mistake. Admit it to yourself and the other person and move on. How long did it take you to make your amends after you were aware you needed to? (Write in the time it took in the blank space next to "Day _____")

What is the average time you made an amend? _____

Does the above time fit your definition for prompt?   Yes _____   No _____

If your answer is no, what is your plan to improve your promptness. Ask five people in the program that you know have done their Step Ten and ask how they worked on promptness. Record your findings below.

1. _____

2. _____

3. _____

4. _____

5. _____

What is the most significant thing you learned about yourself in completing your Step Ten?

_____

_____

_____

On a scale from 1-10, rate yourself on the work you did in Step Ten.

1 2 3 4 5 6 7 8 9 10

Why? _____

_____

Feedback Form

The following space is provided for feedback from your group on your Step One work. Use this feedback page for reflection or for continued work on your Step One. May your future journey of recovery begin with this first step.

Name of Group Member _____ Rating 1   2   3   4   5   6   7   8   9   10

Feedback _____

Name of Group Member _____ Rating 1   2   3   4   5   6   7   8   9   10

Feedback _____

Name of Group Member _____ Rating 1   2   3   4   5   6   7   8   9   10

Feedback _____

Name of Group Member _____ Rating 1   2   3   4   5   6   7   8   9   10

Feedback _____

Name of Group Member _____ Rating 1   2   3   4   5   6   7   8   9   10

Feedback _____

Name of Group Member _____ Rating 1   2   3   4   5   6   7   8   9   10

Feedback _____

Name of Group Member _____ Rating 1   2   3   4   5   6   7   8   9   10

Feedback _____

Name of Group Member _____ Rating 1   2   3   4   5   6   7   8   9   10

Feedback _____

Step #11

"Sought through prayer and meditation to improve our conscious contact with God as we understood Him, praying only for the knowledge of His will for us and the power to carry that out"

Sought

The word *sought* means to seek with the intention to find. This takes time and effort. Do you put time aside to pray and meditate on a regular basis?

Yes _____ No _____

If your answer was no, set aside time to do this daily. Once this time is set, you may or may not want to involve another person to make sure that you are accountable. If you choose to do this, what is their name?

_____

Below, check off if you were able to pray and/or meditate on a daily basis for the next thirty-one days.

Day	Prayer	Meditation
1		
2		
3		
4		
5		
6		
7		
8		
9		
10		
11		
12		
13		
14		
15		
16		
17		
18		
19		
20		
21		
22		
23		
24		
25		
26		
27		
28		
29		
30		
31		

Conscious Contact

What have been some of your "contact" experiences over the past thirty-one days?

_____

_____

_____

Some people journal their contacts with God. Would you like to make that a part of your spiritual life?

Yes _____   No _____

Knowledge Of His Will

Other questions to ask yourself are "Am I praying for the *knowledge of His will?*" If you feel you are doing this, put a "Y" next to the days you are praying. As a Christian, this probably is already be a part of your life. In this step, it is a specific focus for recovery.

What *knowledge of His will* have you gained over the past 31 days?

_____

_____

_____

In what ways has God given you the power to carry out His will as you have understood it during the past 31 days? Be specific.

_____

_____

_____

What is the most significant thing you learned about yourself in completing your Step Eleven?

_____

_____

On a scale from 1-10, rate yourself on the work you did in Step Eleven.

1 2 3 4 5 6 7 8 9 10

Why? _____

_____

Feedback Form

The following space is provided for feedback from your group on your Step One work. Use this feedback page for reflection or for continued work on your Step One. May your future journey of recovery begin with this first step.

Name of Group Member _____ Rating 1   2   3   4   5   6   7   8   9   10

Feedback _____

Name of Group Member _____ Rating 1   2   3   4   5   6   7   8   9   10

Feedback _____

Name of Group Member _____ Rating 1   2   3   4   5   6   7   8   9   10

Feedback _____

Name of Group Member _____ Rating 1   2   3   4   5   6   7   8   9   10

Feedback _____

Name of Group Member _____ Rating 1   2   3   4   5   6   7   8   9   10

Feedback _____

Name of Group Member _____ Rating 1   2   3   4   5   6   7   8   9   10

Feedback _____

Name of Group Member _____ Rating 1   2   3   4   5   6   7   8   9   10

Feedback _____

Name of Group Member _____ Rating 1   2   3   4   5   6   7   8   9   10

Feedback _____

Step #12

"Having had a spiritual awakening as the result of these steps,
we tried to carry this message to others,
and to practice these principles in all our affairs"

Having Had A Spiritual Awakening

In many ways recovery from addiction has brought on several *awakenings*, all of which are spiritual. What were some of the awakenings that you have had in your spiritual life since you have started your addiction recovery?

_____

_____

_____

_____

_____

What part of this *awakening* was a direct result of working the steps? _____

_____

_____

What steps seemed to be more important to you as far as a *spiritual awakening*?_____

_____

_____

Tried To Carry This Message To Others

How have you tried to carry this message during your recovery? _____

_____

_____

_____

How do you intend to carry this message from here on? _____

_____

_____

_____

What are some things you have learned about yourself and others as you have carried the message to others?

_____

_____

_____

_____

What are some experiences you have had in "giving it away?"

_____

_____

_____

_____

How did you feel after giving it away in these experiences?

I felt _____

I felt _____

And To Practice These Principles In All Our Affairs

Continuing the principles of honesty, spirituality, and responsibility for your own behavior, good or bad, and being prompt about admitting is important for a life-style of recovery. This helps to avoid carrying around guilt and shame that can bring you back into an addiction cycle. You deserve the best sobriety that you could ever have. It is in giving it away that you will often find that your own recovery is enhanced.

How have you practiced these principles in the following areas of your life?

Spiritual Life

1. _____

2. _____

3. _____

Emotional Life

1. _____

2. _____

3. _____

Social Life

1. _____

2. _____

3. _____

Physical Health/Exercise

1. _____

2. _____

3. _____

Financially

1. _____

2. _____

3. _____

Parenting

1. _____

2. _____

3. _____

Work Relationships

1. _____

2. _____

3. _____

Family Members

1. _____

2. _____

3. _____

Sexuality

1. _____

2. _____

3. _____

Marriage

1. _____

2. _____

3. _____

What is the most significant thing you learned about yourself completing Step Twelve?

_____

_____

On a scale from 1-10, rate yourself on the work you did in Step Twelve.

1   2   3   4   5   6   7   8   9   10

Why? _____

_____

Feedback Form

The following space is provided for feedback from your group on your Step One work. Use this feedback page for reflection or for continued work on your Step One. May your future journey of recovery begin with this first step.

Name of Group Member _____ Rating 1 2 3 4 5 6 7 8 9 10

Feedback _____

Name of Group Member _____ Rating 1 2 3 4 5 6 7 8 9 10

Feedback _____

Name of Group Member _____ Rating 1 2 3 4 5 6 7 8 9 10

Feedback _____

Name of Group Member _____ Rating 1 2 3 4 5 6 7 8 9 10

Feedback _____

Name of Group Member _____ Rating 1 2 3 4 5 6 7 8 9 10

Feedback _____

Name of Group Member _____ Rating 1 2 3 4 5 6 7 8 9 10

Feedback _____

Name of Group Member _____ Rating 1 2 3 4 5 6 7 8 9 10

Feedback _____

Name of Group Member _____ Rating 1 2 3 4 5 6 7 8 9 10

Feedback _____

Appendix

Feelings Exercise

1. I feel (put feeling word here) when (put a present situation when you feel this).
2. I first remember feeling put the same feeling word here when earliest occurrence of this feeling.

Abandoned	Attractive	Childlike	Demoralized	Exhilarated	Hollow
Abused	Aware	Choked-up	Dependent	Exposed	Honest
Aching	Awestruck	Close	Depressed	Fake	Hopeful
Accepted	Badgered	Cold	Deprived	Fascinated	Hopeless
Accused	Baited	Comfortable	Deserted	Feisty	Horrified
Accepting	Bashful	Comforted	Desirable	Ferocious	Hostile
Admired	Battered	Competent	Desired	Foolish	Humiliated
Adored	Beaten	Competitive	Despair	Forced	Hurried
Adventurous	Beautiful	Complacent	Despondent	Forceful	Hurt
Affectionate	Belligerent	Complete	Destroyed	Forgiven	Hyper
Agony	Belittled	Confident	Different	Forgotten	Ignorant
Alienated	Bereaved	Confused	Dirty	Free	Ignored
Aloof	Betrayed	Considerate	Disenchanted	Friendly	Immature
Aggravated	Bewildered	Consumed	Disgusted	Frightened	Impatient
Agreeable	Blamed	Content	Disinterested	Frustrated	Important
Aggressive	Blaming	Cool	Dispirited	Full	Impotent
Alive	Bonded	Courageous	Distressed	Funny	Impressed
Alone	Bored	Courteous	Distrustful	Furious	Incompetent
Alluring	Bothered	Coy	Distrusted	Gay	Incomplete
Amazed	Brave	Crabby	Disturbed	Generous	Independent
Amused	Breathless	Cranky	Dominated	Gentle	Insecure
Angry	Bristling	Crazy	Domineering	Genuine	Innocent
Anguished	Broken-up	Creative	Doomed	Giddy	Insignificant
Annoyed	Bruised	Critical	Doubtful	Giving	Insincere
Anxious	Bubbly	Criticized	Dreadful	Goofy	Isolated
Apart	Burdened	Cross	Eager	Grateful	Inspired
Apathetic	Burned	Crushed	Ecstatic	Greedy	Insulted
Apologetic	Callous	Cuddly	Edgy	Grief	Interested
Appreciated	Calm	Curious	Edified	Grim	Intimate
Appreciative	Capable	Cut	Elated	Grimy	Intolerant
Apprehensive	Captivated	Damned	Embarrassed	Grouchy	Involved
Appropriate	Carefree	Dangerous	Empowered	Grumpy	Irate
Approved	Careful	Daring	Empty	Hard	Irrational
Argumentative	Careless	Dead	Enraged	Harried	Irked
Aroused	Caring	Deceived	Enraptured	Hassled	Irresponsible
Astonished	Cautious	Deceptive	Enthusiastic	Healthy	Irritable
Assertive	Certain	Defensive	Enticed	Helpful	Irritated
Attached	Chased	Delicate	Esteemed	Helpless	Isolated
Attacked	Cheated	Delighted	Exasperated	Hesitant	Jealous
Attentive	Cheerful	Demeaned	Excited	High	Jittery

Joyous	Positive	Scorned	Suffocated	Used
Lively	Powerless	Scrutinized	Sure	Useful
Lonely	Present	Secure	Sweet	Useless
Loose	Precious	Seduced	Sympathy	Unworthy
Lost	Pressured	Seductive	Tainted	Validated
Loving	Pretty	Self-centered	Tearful	Valuable
Low	Proud	Self-conscious	Tender	Valued
Lucky	Pulled apart	Selfish	Tense	Victorious
Lustful	Put down	Separated	Terrific	Violated
Mad	Puzzled	Sensuous	Terrified	Violent
Maudlin	Quarrelsome	Sexy	Thrilled	Voluptuous
Malicious	Queer	Shattered	Ticked	Vulnerable
Mean	Quiet	Shocked	Tickled	Warm
Miserable	Raped	Shot down	Tight	Wary
Misunderstood	Ravished	Shy	Timid	Weak
Moody	Ravishing	Sickened	Tired	Whipped
Morose	Real	Silly	Tolerant	Whole
Mournful	Refreshed	Sincere	Tormented	Wicked
Mystified	Regretful	Sinking	Torn	Wild
Nasty	Rejected	Smart	Tortured	Willing
Nervous	Rejuvenated	Smothered	Touched	Wiped out
Nice	Rejecting	Smug	Trapped	Wishful
Numb	Relaxed	Sneaky	Tremendous	Withdrawn
Nurtured	Relieved	Snowed	Tricked	Wonderful
Nuts	Remarkable	Soft	Trusted	Worried
Obsessed	Remembered	Solid	Trustful	Worthy
Offended	Removed	Solitary	Trusting	
Open	Repulsed	Sorry	Ugly	
Ornery	Repulsive	Spacey	Unacceptable	
Out of control	Resentful	Special	Unapproachable	
Overcome	Resistant	Spiteful	Unaware	
Overjoyed	Responsible	Spontaneous	Uncertain	
Overpowered	Responsive	Squelched	Uncomfortable	
Overwhelmed	Repressed	Starved	Under control	
Pampered	Respected	Stiff	Understanding	
Panicked	Restless	Stimulated	Understood	
Paralyzed	Revolved	Stifled	Undesirable	
Paranoid	Riled	Strangled	Unfriendly	
Patient	Rotten	Strong	Ungrateful	
Peaceful	Ruined	Stubborn	Unified	
Pensive	Sad	Stuck	Unhappy	
Perceptive	Safe	Stunned	Unimpressed	
Perturbed	Satiated	Stupid	Unsafe	
Phony	Satisfied	Subdued	Unstable	
Pleasant	Scared	Submissive	Upset	
Pleased	Scolded	Successful	Uptight	

The Twelve-Steps of Alcoholics Anonymous

1. We admitted we were powerless over alcohol–that our lives had become unmanageable.

2. Came to believe that a Power greater than ourselves could restore us to sanity.

3. Made a decision to turn our will and our lives over to the care of God as we understood Him.

4. Made a searching and fearless moral inventory of ourselves.

5. Admitted to God, to ourselves, and to another human being the exact nature of our wrongs.

6. Were entirely ready to have God remove all these defects of character.

7. Humbly asked Him to remove our shortcomings.

8. Made a list of all people we had harmed, and became willing to make amends to them all.

9. Made direct amends to such people where ever possible, except when to do so would injure them or others.

10. Continued to take personal inventory, and when we were wrong, promptly admitted it.

11. Sought though prayer and meditation to improve our conscious contact with God as we understood Him, praying only for knowledge of His will for us and the power to carry that out.

12. Having had a spiritual awakening as the result of these steps, we tried to carry this message to others and to practice these principles in all our affairs.

The Twelve-Steps of Alcoholics Anonymous
Adapted for Addicts

1. We admitted we were powerless over our addiction—that our lives had become unmanageable.

2. Came to believe that a Power greater than ourselves could restore us to sanity.

3. Made a decision to turn our will and our lives over to the care of God as we understood Him.

4. Made a searching and fearless moral inventory of ourselves.

5. Admitted to God, to ourselves, and to another human being the exact nature of our wrongs.

6. Were entirely ready to have God remove all these defects of character.

7. Humbly asked God to remove our shortcomings.

8. Made a list of all people we had harmed, and became willing to make amends to them all.

9. Made direct amends to such people wherever possible, except when to do so would injure them or others.

10. Continued to take personal inventory, and when we were wrong, promptly admitted it.

11. Sought through prayer and meditation to improve our conscious contact with God as we understood Him, praying only for knowledge of His will for us and the power to carry that out.

12. Having had a spiritual awakening as the result of these steps, we tried to carry this message to others and to practice these principles in all our day to day living.

Counseling Services

"Without the intensive, my marriage would have ended and I would not have known why. Now I am happier than ever and my marriage is bonded permanently."

Counseling Sessions

Couples are helped through critical phases of disclosure moving into the process of recovery, and rebuilding trust in relationships. We have helped many couples rebuild their relationship and grasp and implement the necessary skills for an intimate relationship.

Individual counseling offers a personal treatment plan for successful healing in your life. In just one session a counselor can help you understand how you became stuck and how to move toward freedom.

Partners of sex addicts need an advocate. Feelings of fear, hurt, anger, betrayal, and grief require a compassionate, effective response. We provide that expert guidance and direction. We have helped many partners heal through sessions that get them answers to their many questions including: "How can I trust him again?"

A counseling session today can begin your personal journey toward healing.

3 and 5 Day Intensives

in Colorado Springs, Colorado are available for the following issues:

· Sexual Addiction Couple or Individual · Partners of Sexual Addicts
· Intimacy Anorexia · Partner Betrayal Trauma

Attendees of Intensives will receive:

• Personal attention from counselors who specialize in your area of need
• An understanding of how the addiction /anorexia and its consequences came into being
• Three appointments daily
• Daily assignments to increase the productiveness of these daily sessions
• Individuals get effective counseling to recover from the effects of sexual addiction, abuse and anorexia
• Addiction, abuse, anorexia issues are thoroughly addressed for couples and individuals. This includes the effects on the partner or family members of the addict, and how to rebuild intimacy toward a stronger relationship.

PRODUCTS FOR MEN'S RECOVERY

The Final Freedom

BOOK: $22.95/$35.00

The Final Freedom gives more current information than many professional counselors have today. In addition to informing sex addicts and their partners about sex addiction, it gives hope for recovery. The information provided in this book would cost hundreds of dollars in counseling hours to receive. Many have attested to successful recovery from this information alone.

101 Freedom Exercises

$39.95

This workbook provides tips, principles, survival techniques and therapeutic homework that has been tested and proven on many recovering sex addicts from all walks of life who have practiced these principles and have maintained their sobriety for many years. Jesus promised us a life of freedom, this book makes this promise a practical journey.

Steps to Freedom

$14.95

The Twelve Steps of recovery have become a major influence in the restoration of this country from the age old problem of alcohol and substance abuse. This book follows in the tradition of the Twelve Steps from a Christian perspective breaking down the various principles for each reader so that they can experience the freedom from sexual addiction.

Partner Betrayal Trauma

DVD:$69.95/COMPANION GUIDE:$11.95

The *Helping Her Heal* DVD paired with this companion guide are both vital tools for the man who has struggled with sexual addiction, exposed his marriage to the fallout of betrayal by acting on his urges, and is now seeking how to help his wife heal from the trauma of this devastating discovery.

Disclosure: Preparing and Completing

$39.95

This information can help the addict and the spouse navigate these often uncharted and misguided waters, saving the addict and the spouse from unnecessary pain or trauma. This DVD can expedite the understanding of each of the significant processes of disclosure for the addict, the spouse, and the marriage.

Healing Her Heart After Relapse

$29.95

This DVD is way more than, "He relapses, he does a consequence and moves on." The addict is given real tools to address the emotional damage and repair of her heart as a result of a relapse. Every couple in recovery would do well to have these tools before a potential relapse.

Boundaries: His. Hers.Ours

$49.95

Boundaries are a healthy, normal, and necessary part of the recovery process for sex addicts, intimacy anorexics, and their spouses. Implementing boundaries in a relationship may seem difficult, but with the proper tools and guidance you can successfully introduce and implement boundaries in your relationship. In this DVD set, Dr. Doug Weiss provides an answer to the clarion call on boundaries by educating and guiding you through this process.

Marriage After Addiction

$29.95

Addiction can have devastating effects on even good marriages. In this DVD you are intelligently guided through the journey you will experience if addiction is part of your marriage story. You will learn important information about the early and later stages of recovery for your marriage.

Shattering Sexualization

$29.95

Dr. Doug Weiss, a Licensed Psychologist who has worked with thousands of men and women struggling with sexualization, will walk you step-by-step as you heal from sexualization and the impact it has had on your life. Start living a life free of sexualization and objectification today!

Series For Men

Clean: A Proven Plan For Men Committed to Sexual Integrity

BOOK: $16.95/DVD:$29.95/JOURNAL:$14.95

Clean is a priceless, no-nonsense resource for every husband, father, brother, son, friend, pastor, and Christian leader on the front lines of this war. It is a soldier's handbook for those ready to reclaim their homes, churches, and nations for the God who has built them to succeed.

Lust Free Living

BOOK:$13.95/DVD:$23.95

Every man can fight for and obtain a lust free lifestyle. Once you know how to stop lust, you will realize how weak lust really can be. God gace you the power to protect those you love from the ravages of lust for the rest of your life! It's time to take it back!

Men Make Men

DVD:$29.95/GUIDEBOOK:$11.95

Dr. Weiss takes the listeners by the hand and step-by-step walks through the creative process God used to make every man into a man of God. This practical teaching on DVD combined with the Men Make Guidebook can revitalize the men in any home or local church.

Addiction Recovery

Recovery for Everyone

BOOK: $22.95/DVD:$99.00/WORKBOOK:$39.95/STEPBOOK: $14.95

Recovery for Everyone helps addicts fight and recover from any addiction they are facing. Learn truths and gain a biblical understanding to break the strongholds in your life.

You will also find an explanation as to how an addiction may have become a part of your life and details as to how you can walk the path to recovery. You will find a roadmap to help you begin and navigate an incredible journey toward freedom. Then you can become part of the solution and even help others get free as well.

Secret Solutions: More Than 100 Ways to End the Secret

$39.95

Female sexual addiction is real and impacting many women's lives today. This Workbook is a practical step-by-step guide for recovery from this growing issue in our culture. The *Secret Solutions*, can be used in conjunction with therapy or as part of Twelve Step relationships or groups you may be a part of. My hope is that you receive the precious gift of recovery as many others have, and that you maintain it the rest of your life, for your benefit and for the benefit of those you love.

PRODUCTS FOR PARTNER'S RECOVERY

Partners: Healing From His Addiction

$14.95

Partners: Healing from His Addiction offers real hope that you can heal from his sexual addictions. After presenting statistics and personal stories, it will walk you down the path to reclaim your life, your voice, and your power, to be who you are without the impact of his addiction.

Partners Recovery Guide: 100 Empowering Exercises

$39.95

The *Partners Recovery Guide : 100 Empowering Exercises* guide was borne out of the latest in Christian self help books research on the effects on a woman who has lived with a sexual addict. This workbook will take you down the clear path of healing from the devastating impact of his sex addiction and accompany you along your entire journey.

Beyond Love: A 12 Step Guide for Partners

$14.95

Beyond Love is an interactive workbook that allows the partners of sex addicts to gain insight and strength through working the Twelve Steps. This book can be used for individual purposes or as a group study workbook.

Partner Betrayal Trauma

BOOK:$22.95/DVD:$65.95

Partner Betrayal Trauma will help you unlock that power by providing an outstanding guide on how to become stronger every day and get past the trauma of betrayal. The pain and experience of betrayal impacts all of your being and relationships. Fix your broken heart, help your relationships, and reclaim your marriage with the necessary strategies for your personal recovery.

Partner Betrayal Trauma: The Workbook

$39.95

In this workbook by Dr. Weiss, you will gain the insight and support you need to understand what betrayal trauma is and how to overcome it to be the strongest version of yourself. This is an excellent guide for those struggling to overcome the past trauma of a betrayal in their relationship.

Partner Betrayal Trauma: Step Guide

$14.95

This is an excellent step-by-step guide for those struggling to overcome the past trauma of a betrayal in their relationship. You will gain insight from a therapist who has worked with countless patients and families for over 30 years to provide them with the support they need to come out the other side whole and better versions of themselves.

He Needs To Change, Dr. Weiss

$29.95

He Needs To Change, Dr. Weiss DVD addresses the pain, trauma, and betrayal women experience because of their partner's sex addiction, betrayal, and/or intimacy anorexia. In this DVD, Dr. Weiss addresses the issue of change that he has explained to thousands of women in his office.

Unstuck for Partners

$29.95

The *Unstuck* DVD is for every woman who has experienced the pain of their partner's sex addiction or intimacy anorexia and feels stuck, confused, frustrated and unable to move on. You didn't sign up for this and honestly, you don't get it! This DVD helps you "get it" so you can process the painful reality you are in and start to live again.

Why Do I Stay, When it Doesn't make Sense

$39.95

In this video, Dr. Doug Weiss utilizes his several decades of experience to give you information and tools that can help you make your decision with mental clarity and confidence. Whether you decide to stay, separate, or divorce, your future can be filled with new opportunities and a life that you genuinely enjoy.

Triggered

$49.00

In the Triggered DVD, Dr. Weiss gives women a repertoire of tools to be successful when a trigger occurs. Triggers are normal for partners of sex addicts, but each woman's triggers are unique and must be navigated in different ways. This DVD can be a life-changing message which will validate your struggles to heal and help you face the challenges of being triggered after partner betrayal trauma.

PRODUCTS FOR INTIMACY ANOREXIA

Helping My Spouse Heal from My Intimacy Anorexia Video Course

$99.00

Are you struggling to validate your spouse's pain from Intimacy Anorexia and help them begin to heal? For the spouse of an intimacy anorexic, the pain is excruciating and sometimes even debilitating. This course is for the intimacy anorexic who is aware of their behaviors and wants to transition into a connected, intimate relationship with their spouse.

Intimacy Anorexia

BOOK:$22.95/DVD:$69.95

This hidden addiction is destroying so many marriages today. In your hands is the first antidote for someone with intimacy anorexia to turn the pages on this addiction process. Excerpts from intimacy anorexics and their spouses help this book become clinically helpful and personal in its impact to communicate hope and healing for the intimacy anorexic and the marriage.

Intimacy Anorexia: The Workbook

$39.95

Intimacy Anorexia is a hidden addiction that is destroying many marriages today. Within the pages of this workbook you will find more than 100 practical and empowering exercises to guide you through your personal recovery towards intimacy. Douglas Weiss has been successfully counseling intimacy anorexics for many years in his practice.

Intimacy Anorexia: The Steps

$14.95

This workbook follows in the tradition of the Twelve-Steps breaking down the various principles for readers so that they can experience freedom from intimacy anorexia. It is our hope that you will join the millions who have received help in their personal recovery using these Twelve-Steps.

Pain for Love

$29.95

Pain For Love describes in detail one of the most insidious strategies of an intimacy anorexic with their spouse. This dynamic is experienced by many who are married to an intimacy anorexic. This paradigm can empower the spouse and help them stop participating in a pain for love dynamic in their marriage.

Sin of Withholding

$49.95

This DVD is the first to address the Biblical foundation of the sin of withholding in believers' hearts. The practical application in marriage addressing Intimacy Anorexia is also interwoven in this revelational teaching on the Sin of Withholding. Once a believer is free of this sin, their walk with the Lord and their fruit towards others can increase expediently.

Narcissism Sex Addiction & Intimacy Anorexia

$29.95

The profound information that you will learn in this DVD will help you fairly evaluate your specific situation for narcissism, which will help you develop a treatment plan to address the issue you are dealing with at its core. Having this clarity can help expedite the healing process for the sex addict, intimacy anorexic, and the spouse, as they are able to tackle the real issue at hand.

Married and Alone

BOOK:$14.95/DVD:$49.95

The impact of being married and alone is very real. Dr. Weiss explains why and will help you to start a journey of recovery from living with a spouse with intimacy or sexual anorexia. My hope is that whatever reason you are watching this DVD you realize that you are worthy of being loved, whether your spouse has decided to pursue recovery or has chosen his or her anorexia over you.

Married and Alone: Healing Exercises for Spouses

$39.95

This workbook is designed to help the spouse heal from the impact of their relationship with an intimacy anorexic which may have been experienced over years or decades. The addiction patterns of an alcoholic, gambler, overeater, sex addict or intimacy anorexic have a direct impact on their spouse's life in so many ways.

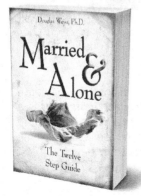

Married and Alone: The Twelve Step Guide

$14.95

This book follows in the tradition of the Twelve-Steps by breaking down the various principles for each reader so that they can experience the discovery of the Twelve-Step promises. It is our hope that you will join the millions who have received help in their recovery by using these Twelve-Steps. These Steps can further your healing and recovery from your spouse's Intimacy Anorexia.

Other Resources

Worthy

WORKBOOK: $29.95/DVD$29.95

The Worthy Workbook and DVD, is designed for a 12 week study. Here is a path that anyone can take to get and stay worthy. Follow this path, and you too will make the journey from worthless to worthy just as others have.

Emotional Fitness

$16.95

Everyone has an unlimited number of emotions, but few have been trained to identify, choose, communicate, and master them. More than a guide for gaining emotional fitness and mastery, in these pages you will find a pathway to a much more fulfilling life.

Letters to My Daughter

$14.95

A gift for your daughter as she enters college. Letters to my Daughter includes my daily letters to my daughter during her first year of college. The letters are about life, God, boys, relationships and being successful in college and life in general.

Born for War

$29.95

Born for War teaches practical tools to defeat these sexual landmines and offers scriptural truths that empower young men to desire successfulness in the war thrust upon them. In this DVD, he equips this generation to win the war for their destiny. It also includes one session for parents to support their son through this battle.

Princes Take Longer Than Frogs

$29.95

This 2 hour DVD helps single women ages 15-30, to successfully navigate through the season of dating. Dr. Weiss' *Princes Take Longer Than Frogs* is a faith-based discussion broken up into several segments including Characteristics of Princes and Frogs, lies women Believe, Dating, Accountability, Boundaries, Sex and the Brain and so much more.

Indestructible

$29.95

The Indestructible series gives you a foundational understanding about your innate design as God's child. Addiction, betrayal, and abuse or neglected can all cause trials in our lives that can trigger feelings of worthlessness and defeat. God's Word reveals that your soul is not capable of being destroyed. Once you recognize and embrace your indestructible nature, you can change how you think, feel, and believe about your past, present, and future!

Sex after Recovery

$59.95

Sex after Recovery will help you navigate a variety of issues including how to reclaim a healthy sexual life together. This DVD set will help you to reclaim and recover your sexuality both individually and with each other.

Sexual Templates

$29.95

Dr. Doug Weiss, a Licensed Psychologist who has worked with thousands of men and women who are sexually addicted, have experienced trauma, or have had negative sexual experiences which have impacted their sexual template, will use his thirty years experience to help you rewire your brain and recreate a new, relational sexual template with your spouse.

I Need to Feel Safe

$29.95

This DVD provides a clear path to processing your desire for safety and creates a roadmap to reclaim safety regardless of your partner or spouse's choices. Dr. Weiss has helped thousands of women rebuild their fractured safety, heal the betrayal, and find hope for themselves. If your heart has cried out to feel safe, this DVD is a response to that heart cry.

Intrigue Addiction:

$29.95

The intrigue addict is constantly on the hunt for a look or gesture from another person that insinuates they are attracted to or interested in them. The intrigue addiction can go unnoticed, but it can create just as much pain for the spouse as other sexually addictive behaviors.

Prodigal Parent Process Resources

Prodigal Parent Process

BOOK: $19.95/DVD$59.95

Dr. Weiss, drawing upon his thirty-plus years of experience working with prodigals and parents of prodigals, delivers biblical and practical tools to aid you in your journey to hope and healing. You can't change the fact that you have a prodigal but you can set your mind upon how you will go through this journey with your prodigal.

Prodigal Parent Process Workbook

$16.95

In conjunction with the Parent Prodigal Process videos and book, this workbook helps you therapeutically work through deep-rooted struggles related to being a parent of a prodigal. Working through this series and workbook will prompt serious internal dialogue with yourself as it relates to your prodigal child.

Marriage Resources

Lover Spouse

$13.95

This book provides guidelines to lead a prosperous married life and is helpful for anyone wanting to know more about what the Lord Almighty desires for your love and marriage. Featured with practical tips and foundational relationship skills, the information offered in this book will guide couples through the process of creating an intimate Christian marriage based on a solid biblical worldview.

Upgrade Your Sex Life

BOOK:$16.95/DVD:$29.95

Upgrade Your Sex Life actually teaches you own unique sexual expression that you and your partner are pre-wired to enjoy. Once you learn what your type is, you can communicate and have sex on a more satisfying level.

Servant Marriage

$13.95

Servant Marriage book is a Revelation on God's Masterpiece of marriage. In these pages, you will walk with God as He creates the man, the woman and his masterpiece called marriage.

Marriage Mondays

$59.95

This is an eight week marriage training that actually gives you the skills to have a healthy, more vibrant marriage. Each week Dr. Weiss tackles major aspects of marriage from a biblical perspective. Apply these techniques and it will transform your marriage. This course provides couples to grow their marriages either in a small group setting or as their very own private marriage retreat.

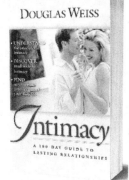

Intimacy: 100 Day Guide to a Lasting Relationship

$11.99

The *Intimacy: A 100 Day Guide to Lasting Relationships* book gives you a game plan to improve your relationships. Intimacy doesn't need to be illusive! It's time to recognize intimacy for what it is – a loving and lifelong process that you can learn and develop.

A·A·S·A·T

American Association for Sex Addiction Therapy

Sex Addiction Training Set

$1195

Both men and women are seeking to counsel more than ever for sexually addictive behaviors. You can be prepared! Forty-seven hours of topics related to sexual addiction treatment are covered in this training including:
- The Six Types of Sex Addicts
- Sex and Recovery
- Neurological Understanding
- Relapse Strategies

Partner's Recovery Training Set

$995

With this AASAT training, you will gain proven clinical insight into treating the issues facing partners. You can be prepared! Thirty-nine hours of topics related to partners treatment are covered in this training, including:
- Partner Model
- Anger
- Partner Grief
- Boundaries

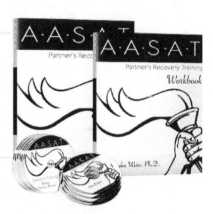

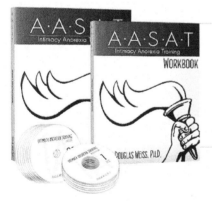

Intimacy Anorexia Training Set

$995

This growing issue of Intimacy Anorexia will need your competent help in your community. Now, you can be prepared to identify it and treat it. In this training you'll cover topics like:
- Identifying Intimacy Anorexia
- Treatment Plan
- Causes of Intimacy Anorexia
- Relapse Strategies

For more information visit www.aasat.org or call 719.330.2425

Struggling with Trauma, Anxiety, and PTSD?

Trauma, anxiety, and PTSD can imbalance your brain. When your brain is out of balance, or stuck, you don't feel right and it's impossible to function at your highest level. Cereset is a proven technology that's non-invasive and highly effective. Cereset can help your brain free itself, enabling you to achieve higher levels of well-being and balance throughout your life.

Cereset – Garden of the Gods is located at Heart to Heart Counseling Center in Colorado Springs, Colorado and specializes in working with sexual addiction, intimacy anorexia, betrayal trauma, PTSD, anxiety, and more.

Here's what clients had to say about Cereset Garden of the Gods after their sessions:

"Cereset helped save our marriage. My husband and I both did Cereset and with it helping both of us be calmer and sleep better, we respond to each other in a more loving and respectful way. I notice a big change in him, and he says the same about me. After the sessions I noticed a marked improvement in my sleep and my ability to stay calm during moments that would trigger an argument with my spouse prior to Cereset. Before Cereset we felt chaotic and now, afterwards, we both feel more at peace. our household is a is a calm place to be now and we are so grateful!"

"I've noticed a significant improvement in my ability to control and correct my patterns of thought – specifically negative thoughts. I also noticed my reaction to negative events was calmer and more controlled instead of being thrown in a downward spiral. I'm more able to recognize and deal with stress."

"As a health care provider, I would refer patients for Cereset. I suffered from extreme sleeplessness; difficulty falling asleep and staying asleep. I did not sleep more than 2-3 hours a night for years. By the week's end I slept 7 hours a night! I also suffered from extreme anxiety and PTSD, which after years led to depression and feelings of hopelessness/helplessness. My anxiety has significantly improved. You were amazing, professional, knowledgeable, and tailored to my needs very well. Cereset produces results. If you are on the fence about this, trust the evidence-based studies and the thousands of positive testimonials. You will NOT regret it."

View a client
testimonial here

Schedule Your Cereset Intensive Today!

The cost for five sessions
(one per day) is $1,500.

For more information call us at 719-644-5778

Recovery Meetings

1. Any new members are introduced by the point person and are asked to verbalize the Recovery Covenant to the group in the first person. (For example, I covenant to...)

2. Introductions - Beginning with the chairperson of the meeting, introductions are done as follows: The chairperson introduces themselves, shares their feelings, their boundaries and length of time free from those behaviors.

Example:
"My name is John. I feel frustrated and alone. My boundaries to stay free are no pornography, bookstores, and no sex outside of marriage. I worked on Exercises Nos. 5-7 in my Freedom for Everyone workbook and made four pages of progress on my Steps to Recovery workbook since our last meeting. I have been free for 3 weeks."

3. The *chairperson* chooses a topic related to staying free from being driven by addiction that the group discusses. Each member can share without feedback from the group, unless feedback is specifically asked for by the sharing member.

4. Honest Time - Group members break off into groups of two to three members and discuss thoughts, behaviors, struggles and successes since the last meeting (James 5:16).

5. Closing Prayer - Group members come back together to repeat the Lord's Prayer.

Recovery Group Materials

1. *Freedom For Everyone*
2. *Freedom For Everyone: Workbook*
3. *Freedom for Everyone: Steps*

Freedom Group Topics for Discussion

Triggers	Honesty	God's Grace
Fear	Hope	Exercise
Bottom Lines	Relapse	Intimacy
Control	H.A.L.T.	Steps 1-12
Boundaries	Prayer	Maximized Thinking
Recovery Rituals	Feelings	Anger
Dangerous Dabbling	Fun	Father Issues
Sexual Abuse	Grooming Victims	Objectifying
Accountability	Discipline	Acts of Love
My Calling	My Future	Daily Struggles
Dangerous Places	What Works	Dating My Spouse
Control	Male Friends	Humility
Turning It Over	One Day at a Time	My Daily God Time
My Worst Moment	The Gift of Recovery	What God is Doing
Addictions in My Family	Breaking the Curse for My Children	

...And any other topic the chairperson feels is appropriate. Remember, don't be graphic, be honest!

Recovery Groups

What are Recovery Groups?

Recovery Groups are Christ-based support groups for people wanting freedom from being driven by addiction.

How do they work?

One person, impressed by the Holy Spirit who desires to assist helping others obtain freedom from being driven by addiction, asks their pastor to sponsor this ministry. This *point person* will be the contact person for the church. The church will refer people who feel driven by their addiction to the *point person*. This *point person* will meet with those desiring help and will cover the *Recovery Principles* and *Recovery Covenant* with them. Once the person agrees to the *Freedom Principles* and *Freedom Covenant*, they are given the group location and time.

Recovery Group Roles

1. The *point person* serves as the contact person for anyone interested in attending the group. This is to protect the group from someone just dropping in unexpectedly. The *point person* can serve for an indefinite amount of time but should be reconsidered after one year of service.

2. The *chairperson* of the meeting is responsible to start the meeting by asking the point man if any new people need to make a Freedom Covenant. If there are no new Recovery Covenants to be addressed, the chairperson starts the introductions and chooses the topic for the group discussion. The *chairperson* serves the group for a maximum of 8 weeks.   At that time, someone else volunteers to chair the meeting.

Recovery Principles for the First 100 Days of Recovery

1. Pray - Pray in the morning asking Jesus to keep you free today.
2. Read - Read the Bible and read recovery-related material.
3. Meetings - Attend every meeting possible.
4. Call - Call someone in your group and check in with that person at the beginning of each day.
5. Pray - Pray in the evening, thanking God for keeping you free today.

One-Year Recovery Covenant

1. The members of the Recovery Group covenant to total confidentiality of all group members and discussions held during group meetings.

2. Members covenant to attend the Recovery Group for one year and to work through the Recovery Materials and report progress to the group.

3. Members covenant to keep the Recovery Principles for the first 100 days of their journey toward freedom.

Made in the USA
Coppell, TX
15 November 2024

40303967R00077